THE NAME SERIES PICTURE BOOK

NOAH
EMMA
&
BELLE HOPE

Written by A.E. Cosby~Illustrations by Alana Cosby

NOAH

Hebrew

PEACEFUL * PROVIDER OF COMFORT

Nahum 1:7

The Lord is good, a strong hold in the day of trouble; and he knows them that trust in him.

"Noah, what's that behind your back?"
Shouldn't you be helping us pack?

Dad had no idea about his latest find.
Hopefully a new kitten he wouldn't mind.

Before another move with the military
Noah couldn't let this Rescue tarry.

"I'll keep good watch!"
Was usually Noah's caring, comforting way.
"You get to tell Mom", Dad proclaimed.

EMMA

Old German

ALL EMBRACING * WHOLE * ABSOLUTE FAITH

Mark 11:24
Therefore I say to you, whatever things you ask when you pray, believe that you receive them, and you will have them.

Whenever Emma was around
No one ever felt low to the ground.

She had a way to lift you up…
Always seeing the 'full side of the cup'.

"Come on! Let's ALL go take a walk".
Leaving a smile on everyone's face,
she would help you win your race.

"We're in this together!" Wasn't just talk-
Never leaving anyone out.

Emma knew that sharing love—
was what life's all about.

BELLE

French

BEAUTIFUL * BLESSED

Psalm 104:33

I will sing unto the Lord as long as I live: I will sing praise
to my God while I have my being.

HOPE

Old English

TRUST IN THE FUTURE * UNDERSTANDING HEART

Psalm 37:4

Delight yourself also in the LORD, and he shall give you
the desires of your heart.

Whether on a stage
or behind the scenes...

Belle Hope would draw the shyest person out of their cage.
Her voice would float and fill the air~~~

Inviting everyone to stop and stare.

"Keep your view on the beauty that is all around...
Then hope will continuously abound."

"Keep a song in your heart!"
    "Then the blues will never start."

As she spread songs like flowers throughout the day
Belle Hope left you humming on your way.

True beauty comes from within
When you allow God to be your friend.